Three pots of gold

and other stories

Hannie Truijens

Three pots of gold page 2

The three wishes page 10

Tiger, tiger page 18

Nelson

Three pots of gold

Long ago a greedy giant lived
in a castle on the hill.
He liked food and drink.
He liked to sleep.
But he liked gold best of all.

One day a poor boy walked past the castle.
He heard that the giant was asleep so he looked inside and saw a big pot of gold.
He took two pieces and went away.

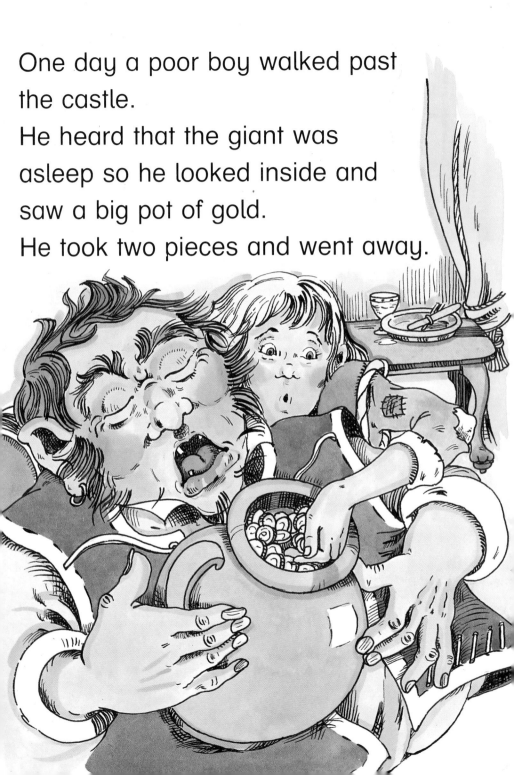

The next day the boy went to the castle with a big sack.

"I have some magic sand," he said to the giant.

"I can turn your pot of gold into three pots of gold."

"Oh ho," said the giant, "I have one
hundred pieces of gold.
If your magic sand works I will
have three hundred pieces."
The boy said, "Give me one piece
of gold and I will show you."

The boy put the piece of gold
into his sack and put some magic
sand on it.
He told the giant to close his
eyes and to say,
"One pot, two
pots, three pots of gold".

6

The giant said,
"One pot, two pots,
three pots of gold,"
and then opened his eyes.
"Look in the sack," said the boy.
The giant found three pieces of
gold in the sack.
He was very, very pleased.

The giant put all his gold
into the sack.
The boy put all his magic sand
on the gold.
"You must say the magic words
one hundred times," said the boy.

The giant closed his eyes and
started to count.
Long before he got to a hundred
times he was fast asleep.
And the boy was already
far away with the sack of gold.

The three wishes

A poor man and his wife lived
near the sea.
One day the woman found a fish
on the sand.
She wanted to take it home
to eat.

The fish said,
"Please put me back in the sea."
The woman was sorry for the fish
and she put it back.
"I will give you three wishes,"
it said.

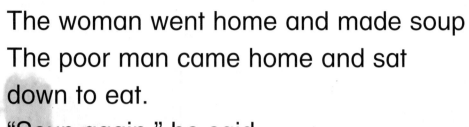

The woman went home and made soup
The poor man came home and sat
down to eat.
"Soup again," he said.
"Every day we have soup.
I wish we had some sausages."

As he said this, some sausages
dropped into his plate.
"That is one wish gone,"
said his wife.
She told him about the fish and
the three wishes.

"Silly woman," said the poor man.
"Why didn't you tell me at once?"
His wife also got cross.
"I wish the sausages were
on your nose," she said.

Up jumped the sausages,
on to the poor man's nose.
Another wish was gone.
The woman forgot to be cross when
she saw his silly long nose.

The man pulled at the sausages
but they would not come off.
His wife helped him but it was
no use.
"Oh, I wish that I had never
wished for sausages," he said.

That was the last wish.
The sausages were gone.
The two of them looked down at
their plates.
They had been very silly and they
still only had soup.

Tiger, tiger

Prem was bored.

His brothers and sisters were too busy to play with him.

His Mum and Dad were too busy to listen to him.

He sat on a tree and wished that a tiger would eat them up.

Prem started to think about
tigers – big, strong tigers with
big, strong teeth.
He heard a noise in the grass.
He didn't stop to look.
He ran home and shouted,
"Tiger, tiger."

19

His brothers and sisters stopped working and ran inside.

His Mum picked him up and ran inside.

His Dad took his gun to go and shoot the tiger.

But there was no tiger.

Prem was happy.

His brothers and sisters had
listened to him.

Mum and Dad had listened to him.

All because of the tiger.

But they soon forgot the tiger,
and Prem was still bored.

A week later Prem played the
same trick.
He shouted, "Tiger, tiger."
They all ran inside.
His Dad took his gun to go and
shoot the tiger.
But there was no tiger.

The next day Prem was playing
near the trees.
He heard a noise in the grass.
"Tiger, tiger," he shouted.
But no one would listen to him.
And no one would pick him up.
"It's a **REAL TIGER**," he shouted.

It was his Dad in a tiger skin.
"You mustn't shout when there is
no tiger," he said.
"You see, no one will listen to
you when there is a real tiger."
"I'm sorry, Dad," said Prem.
"I will never do it again."